WELCOME CURIOUS CATS EVERYWHERE!

Are you ready for an exciting seek-and-find adventure? Think you've got what it takes to travel around the globe and track down our elusive, furry feline friend? Then get ready for a journey like no other!

Cat has packed his bags and set off on a whirlwind trip around the world.

He's hopped on planes...

Scaled mountains...

Swum in the big blue ocean...

Zoomed around on skateboards...

Dashed around on bikes...

Journeyed by boat...

And whizzed around in helicopters to visit every corner of the world.

**Now it's your chance to try and track him down!
Can you find him in sunny Spain? Will you spot him in chilly Antarctica?
Or maybe you'll uncover him in blustery Chicago.**

Each continent is packed full of fascinating things to spot - from iconic buildings to incredible creatures big and small, marvellous mountains and so much more!

Discover incredible facts about each amazing continent.

Then turn the page and see if you can spot Cat!

**So what are you waiting for?
Pack your bags and get ready to...**

CATCH CAT

NORTH AMERICA

Made up of the United States of America, Canada and Mexico, North America is the third largest continent in the world. Dry deserts, huge mountains, lush plains and frozen ground are all a part of its diverse terrain. It's home to millions of people, countless creatures big and small, natural wonders and outstanding man made structures. Read all about some of the amazing things you can find here and then turn the page to see if you can spot them!

CACTI

Cacti usually grow in soil that is dry and rocky, and can be found in deserts all across the world. There are roughly 2,000 different kinds and they come in all sorts of different shapes and sizes. Instead of leaves they are covered in little spiky thorns called spines. They have thick waxy skin which protects them from the heat and contain water in their stems. Some cacti can live for up to 300 years!

ROYAL CANADIAN MOUNTED POLICE

Known as 'Mounties' for short, they are the national police force of Canada. They are famous for their bright red uniforms and broad-brimmed hats called Stetsons. They are also well known for The Musical Ride which is a ceremony where 32 Mounties show off their horse-riding skills, accompanied by music. It has its origins in 1974 when officers used their usual drills accompanied by music to entertain themselves during the evening while they were off duty.

MOUNT RUSHMORE

THE GOLDEN GATE BRIDGE

Opened in 1937, the Golden Gate Bridge is one of the Seven Wonders of the Modern World. Measuring 2,737 metres long, the bridge is hung from two cables each of which is made of 27,572 strands of wire. There are six lanes in total across the bridge and it's estimated that more than *two billion* cars have used the bridge since it opened!

Mount Rushmore is a massive sculpture carved into the huge granite batholith in South Dakota. The sculpture represents four presidents of the United States: George Washington, Thomas Jefferson, Theodore Roosevelt and Abraham Lincoln. It took around 14 years to make, with over 400 people working on the larger-than-life sculpture. Dynamite was used to create the sculpture, along with a process called 'honeycombing' where holes were drilled closely together, allowing small pieces to be removed by hand.

PRAIRIE DOG

Prairie dogs aren't really dogs! They are more closely related to squirrels and got their name because of their dog-like bark. These little creatures build large burrows underground with lots of different entrances. They are made up of long tunnels with little chambers. Some of the chambers even have specific uses - just like in a house! There are chambers for young prairie dogs, chambers for night-time and even special chambers to listen out for predators!

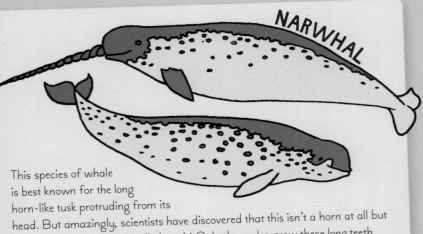

NARWHAL

This species of whale is best known for the long horn-like tusk protruding from its head. But amazingly, scientists have discovered that this isn't a horn at all but is actually a very long, spiralled tooth! Only the males grow these long teeth and they can measure up to three metres in length.

YELLOWSTONE NATIONAL PARK

Covering roughly 9,000 square kilometres, Yellowstone National Park is covered in geysers and hot springs. Old Faithful is the most famous of all of the park's geysers and people come from all over the world to see it erupt. The park is home to several predators including black bears, coyotes, grizzly bears, pumas and wolves.

AMERICAN BISON

These massive shaggy beasts are the national mammal of the United States. In prehistoric times, millions of these creatures grazed all over the plains of North America, but today they can mostly only be found in national parks and other protected wildlife areas. Certain birds will catch a ride on the backs of bison and gobble up any insects they find hiding in their fur.

The White House is home to the President of the United States. It has 132 rooms, 35 bathrooms, 412 doors, 147 windows, 28 fireplaces, 8 staircases, 3 elevators and 6 levels! Phew! Roughly 70,000 people visit the White House *every single day!*

THE WHITE HOUSE

YELLOW TAXIS

The iconic yellow taxicab is an essential part of New York City life! There are roughly 13,000 of them whizzing through the streets of NYC, and day or night they are ready to pick up commuters in need of a lift. Apparently, the first taxis in the US were red and green! It wasn't until the 1960s that a law was introduced stating that all cabs had to be the same colour. How many can you spot zooming around the city?

US SPACE AND ROCKET CENTRE

Packed full of amazing rocket and space equipment, simulators and interactive exhibits, this incredible museum is a fantastic way to learn everything you ever wanted to know about space. One of the most impressive artefacts at the museum is the Space Shuttle Orbiter Pathfinder. It was created in 1977 as a test simulator and is made out of wood and steel.

GREEN SEA TURTLE

Green sea turtles are one of the world's largest species of turtle, but when they are born they are just five centimetres long! Their shells are usually brown, olive, yellow or black, which might make you wonder where they get their name from. Well, they actually have a layer of green fat that lies underneath their shell. Scientists think this is because of their 'green diet' of seaweed!

SOUTH AMERICA

South America is home to the longest river in the world, the Amazon River. It stretches on for over 4,000 miles and is surrounded by another record-breaker – the world's largest rainforest! South America plays host to a kaleidoscope of wildlife found in the lush rainforest, busy city streets and even in the freezing glaciers in the south. Turn the page and see if you can spot all of these South American treasures!

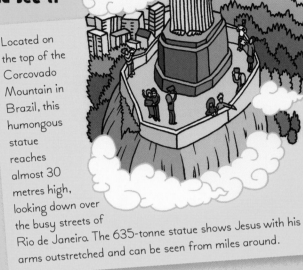

CHRIST THE REDEEMER

Located on the top of the Corcovado Mountain in Brazil, this humongous statue reaches almost 30 metres high, looking down over the busy streets of Rio de Janeiro. The 635-tonne statue shows Jesus with his arms outstretched and can be seen from miles around.

PINK DOLPHINS

These wonderfully colourful creatures make their home in the fresh water of the Amazon River. They spend most of their time at the bottom of the riverbed looking for crabs and turtles to eat. Amazingly, these creatures can rotate their heads up to 180 degrees!

SLOTHS

Found in the Amazon Rainforest, these slow-moving creatures can sometimes be difficult to spot. Hanging upside down in the branches of trees, moss grows on their fur, camouflaging them from hungry predators. Sloths can sleep for up to ten hours every day, only leaving the safety of their trees once a week to go to the toilet!

FOOTBALL

Football is the most popular sport in South America and the continent is home to several world-class football stadiums. The Maracanã stadium in Rio de Janeiro is the second biggest in South America and can hold up to 79,000 people. It was used for the 2016 Olympics as well as two World Cup tournaments.

CARNIVAL

Carnival in Brazil is full of bright costumes, dazzling headdresses, colourful floats, lots of dancing and loud, lively music. The celebration is held 40 days before Easter and it can gather crowds of up to *two million* people! During the parade, men, women and children dance to the sound of live music, making the streets come to life.

BOLIVIAN BOWLER HAT

Lots of women wear these hats in Bolivia. The story goes that shortly after the hats were invented in the 1920s, two brothers from Manchester had a bright idea of selling the hats to British railway employees working in Bolivia at the time. When the hats arrived in South America they realised that they were too small to fit the men! So they sold them to Bolivian women instead, telling them that it was the latest fashion trend in Europe and everyone was wearing one. The craze caught on and the rest is history!

GAUCHO

Gauchos are the cowboys of South America. These skilled horsemen herd huge groups of cattle and are famed for their lasso-throwing skills. Their traditional outfit is a big hat, a colourful shirt, a large poncho and baggy pants called bombachas, which they tuck into their leather boots.

These tea-cupped-sized frogs spend their days fast asleep on large tropical leaves. They wake at night and hunt for their tasty dinner of crickets, flies and moths using their long, sticky tongues. They startle predators by flashing their big red eyes at them, giving them the chance to hop away to safety.

RED-EYED TREE FROGS

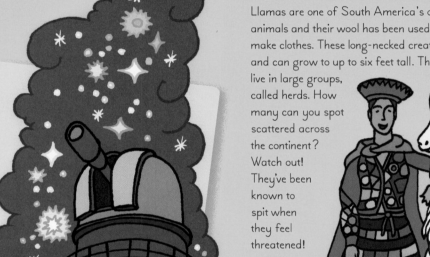

LA SILLA OBSERVATORY

With 13 telescopes to study the night sky, La Silla is one of the biggest observatories in the Southern Hemisphere. The observatory sits on top of the 2,400-metre-high La Silla mountain in the Atacama Desert. This desert is the perfect spot for stargazing as there is no air pollution and no artificial light to drown out the brightness of the stars.

Llamas are one of South America's oldest domesticated animals and their wool has been used for thousands of years to make clothes. These long-necked creatures are related to camels and can grow to up to six feet tall. They are social animals and live in large groups, called herds. How many can you spot scattered across the continent? Watch out! They've been known to spit when they feel threatened!

LLAMAS

MOAI STATUES

Easter Island is scattered with hundreds of massive Moai statues. These gigantic heads were sculpted by the early Rapa Nui people. Some reach over ten metres tall and can weigh up to 80 tonnes! Although the statues are often called heads they do actually have shoulders and arms, buried beneath the ground. Nobody really knows why the statues were built – some think it was for religious purposes, others think they brought good luck. It's a mystery!

When most people think about South America they think of the lush green rainforest, exotic jungle animals and warm tropical weather. But believe it or not, the south of the continent is covered in icy glaciers! The Perito Moreno Glacier stretches out for over 18 icy miles. The surrounding waters are even home to penguins!

PENGUINS

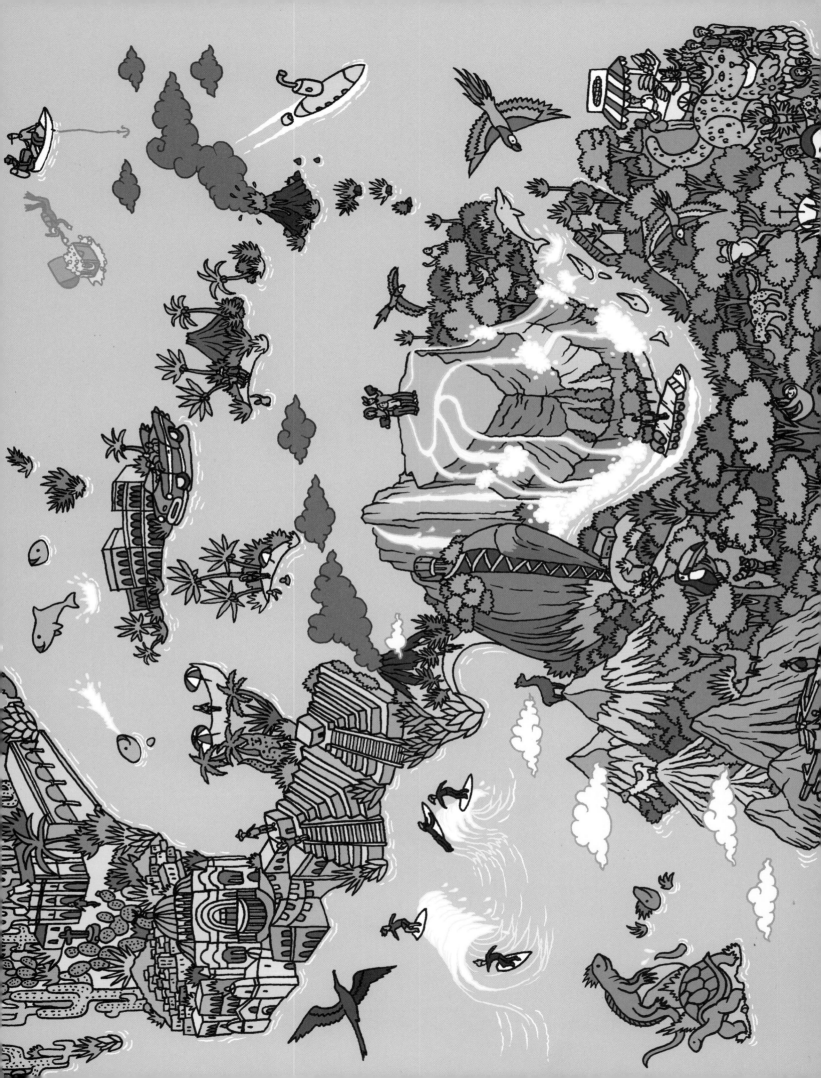

EUROPE

Made up of over 50 countries, Europe is home to more than 740 million people. Travel through Europe and you'll learn all about a variety of cultures, countless religions, and hear more than 200 spoken languages. Some of the most iconic natural and man made tourist attractions can be found here. Uncover facts about this incredibly diverse place and then turn the page to see what you can spot.

This little statue, which sits in the harbour in Copenhagen in Denmark, was created in 1913 to celebrate the story of *The Little Mermaid*, written by Hans Christian Andersen. Inspired by a ballet performance of the story and sculpted to look like the ballerina, Ellen Price, this little mermaid has become the symbol of the city of Copenhagen.

THE LITTLE MERMAID

NORTHERN LIGHTS

Also called the Aurora Borealis, these wonderfully colourful lights dance across the sky and are one of the Seven Natural Wonders of the World. They are created by electronically charged particles from the Sun that enter the Earth's atmosphere when solar winds are powerful. This sounds very technical, but the end result is incredibly beautiful. The magical display can be seen from lots of different places but one of the best spots to see them is in Finland. Can you see them glittering in the sky on the next page?

BIG BEN

Big Ben is actually the name of the 13-tonne bell inside this enormous clock tower in London, UK. Everything about the clock is huge - its minute hand weighs roughly 100 kilograms and is over 3 metres long and the pendulum, which beats every 2 seconds, is 4 metres long and weighs over 310 kilograms! In 1949 the clock slowed by four and a half minutes because a group of starlings perched on the minute hand!

Built between 447 and 432 BC, this enormous temple in Athens was built to worship Athena, the Goddess of Wisdom and Courage. The people of Athens built the huge temple so they could thank Athena for her protection. The Parthenon is one of the most popular tourist attractions and over seven million people come to visit it every year.

At one point there were nearly 10,000 windmills scattered across the Netherlands. Only about 1,000 are left today, but they still remain an iconic symbol of the Dutch landscape and tourists come from all around to see them. There is even a National Windmill Day in mid-May, when windmills are decorated with flowers and Dutch flags.

PARTHENON

WINDMILLS

Serbia is home to a small population of brown bears - although there is nothing small about these creatures! They can grow to up to two metres tall and weigh over 300 kilograms! They are omnivores, which means they eat absolutely everything including berries, meat, honey, ants and even grass if there's nothing else around. They hibernate during the winter, all the way until spring. Shh - don't wake them!

BROWN BEAR

The Sami are a group of people that live in Lapland - an area in the northernmost regions of Finland and Sweden. Sami people have their own language and traditionally have a variety of livelihoods but are best known for reindeer herding. Some Sami still wear the brightly coloured traditional clothing, easily recognised by bands of bright red and yellow patterns against a vibrant blue.

SAMI PEOPLE

BRAN CASTLE

A national monument of Romania, Bran Castle was completed in 1388 to defend Transylvania's border. However, it is better known as the home of Bram Stoker's vampire and is often called Dracula's Castle. Although Dracula is fictional there is a real-life scary story linked to the castle... Queen Marie, who owned the castle in the 1900s, loved it so much that she decided that when she died she wanted her heart to be removed from her body and buried next to the castle!

STARI MOST

Found in Mostar in Bosnia and Herzegovina, this humpbacked Old Bridge was built in the 16th century and rebuilt in 2004 after it was destroyed in the Bosnian war. Today the bridge is used as part of a diving competition. After months of training, contestants jump from the highest point into the icy water below. An extremely dangerous and cold activity!

UKRAINIAN EASTER EGGS

These aren't like the chocolate Easter eggs you find in the supermarket. This tradition of decorating eggs is called Pysanka (meaning 'to write') and is done by applying patterns of wax with a special little instrument called a stylus. When the egg is dipped in dye, only the areas that don't have wax on them will come out coloured. The wax is then melted off to reveal the pattern. How many colourful eggs can you find?

THE BOOK OF KELLS

The Book of Kells is an ancient, hand-written manuscript that is over 1,200 years old and is on permanent display in Trinity College in Dublin, Ireland. It was created by Celtic monks around 800 AD and the pages are full of detailed pictures of humans, animals and mythical beasts. In 1006 it was stolen, but thankfully it was recovered some time later (although without its jewel-covered gold jacket).

AUSTRIAN COWS

Every year in Austria cattle are decorated and herded down from the mountains where they spent the summer grazing in the Alpine meadows. Covered in flowers, ribbons, mirrors and bells, the cows return to the valleys as music plays and people dance in a festival known as 'Almabtrieb'.

Located in Sicily in Italy, Mount Etna is one of the most active volcanoes in Europe and has been blowing out steam and lava since 1500 BC. Measuring about 3,350 metres high, the volcano covers an area of roughly 1,600 kilometres squared. The rich volcanic soil around Mount Etna is perfect for growing grapes, which is why Sicily is famous for its production of wine.

MOUNT ETNA

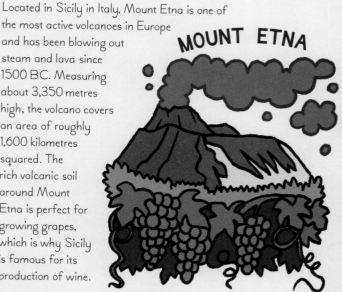

AFRICA

Africa is made up of lots of different countries, cultures and landscapes. It is the second-largest continent in the world and is home to the world's longest river, the River Nile. It also has a lot of wildlife – especially large mammals like antelopes, giraffes, elephants, lions, hyaena, apes and so much more. Uncover facts about this amazing continent and then turn the page to see what you can spot!

THE GREAT PYRAMID OF GIZA

Pyramids are huge stone structures that were built as burial tombs for ancient Egyptian pharaohs. The largest pyramid was built by Pharaoh Khufu around 2550 BC. It measures 147 metres tall and it's thought that 2.3 million blocks were used to build it!

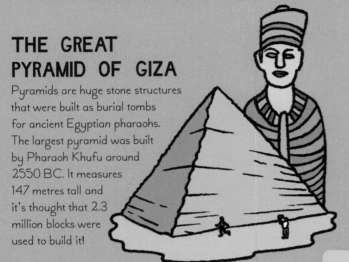

VICTORIA FALLS

Victoria Falls is the world's largest waterfall and measures roughly 1,700 metres wide and 108 metres tall. It has been named one of the Seven Natural Wonders of the World and tourists travel from all around to see it. At night it's possible to see a 'moonbow', which is formed by the reflection of the moonlight on the water.

THE BIG FIVE

The Big Five animals in Africa are the roaring lion, the speedy leopard, the stomping rhinoceros, the trumpeting elephant and the grazing Cape buffalo. Tourists travel from all around the world to go on safari in the hope of catching a glimpse of these magnificent beasts.

Nelson Mandela was a civil rights leader who fought against the apartheid system – which meant that people were kept separate because of the colour of their skin. His protests meant that he spent a lot of his life in prison, but he would eventually become the president of South Africa. He was awarded the Nobel Peace Prize and over 250 other awards for his bravery and courage. Many statues have been put up around the world to honour him.

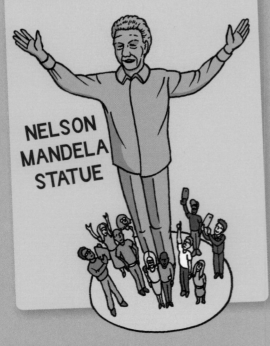

NELSON MANDELA STATUE

Nearly 1,000 years ago this church was built entirely out of a type of volcanic rock – not from the ground up, but chiselled into the earth in the very spot where the rock was found. The rock was shaped to create walls, doors, windows, columns, roof until finally the end result was this enormous church in the shape of a cross.

THE CHURCH OF ST GEORGE

BAOBAB TREE

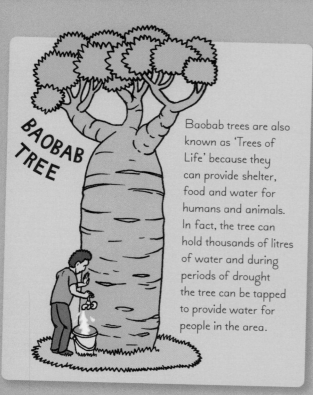

Baobab trees are also known as 'Trees of Life' because they can provide shelter, food and water for humans and animals. In fact, the tree can hold thousands of litres of water and during periods of drought the tree can be tapped to provide water for people in the area.

Mount Kilimanjaro is a dormant volcano and the last time it erupted was over 360,000 years ago. It is the highest mountain in Africa and reaches 5,895 metres high into the sky. The first people to climb this enormous mountain were Hans Meyer, Ludwig Purtscheller and a local called Lauwo in 1889. Nowadays roughly 25,000 people try to climb the summit every year but usually only about two-thirds of them succeed.

MOUNT KILIMANJARO

FENNEC FOX

Fennec foxes are the smallest of all the world's foxes, measuring just 20 centimetres tall. Their huge-bat-like ears get rid of any extra heat and keep them cool in the hot desert temperatures. They spend their days asleep in their underground dens but come night-time, these tiny creatures are busy hunting and playing together.

MOUNTAIN GORILLA

There are only several hundred of these creatures left in the wild. Their diet consists of leaves, stems, shoots and fruit and a full-grown adult will eat over 18 kilograms of food in one day! Can you spot one stomping through the trees?

These bizarre-looking creatures look like they must be related to zebras, but in fact they are the only living relative of the giraffe! The rainforests of central Africa are the only place in the world where they are found in the wild. Their stripes are sometimes called 'follow me' stripes as the bold pattern makes it easy for calves to follow their mothers through the dark forest.

OKAPI

Gelada baboons live in the high mountain meadows in Ethiopia and spend their time sitting on their padded bums munching on grass and herbs. At night these creatures huddle together and sleep on the edges of cliffs!

GELADA BABOONS

AFRICAN GOLDEN CAT

These wild cats are reddish-brown in colour and some have spots on their fur. They are agile climbers but spend most of their life on the ground, tracking their prey and pouncing on them at just the right moment.

ASIA

Asia covers an area of around 45 million square kilometres, making it the largest continent on Earth. It is also the most populated continent in the world and is home to over four billion people! Asia is made up of 48 different countries, each with their own unique customs, cultures and traditions.

MATRYOSHKA DOLL

Also known as a Russian doll or stacking doll, these little wooden toys stack one inside the other. The first set of dolls was made in 1890 and presented at the World's Fair in Paris, where it won a bronze medal in the toy division! The largest set was made in 2003. It contains 51 dolls and the biggest one is almost 54 centimetres tall!

CHERRY BLOSSOM

Cherry blossoms, known as 'sakura', are Japan's national flower. They are a symbol for spring in Japan and represent renewal and hope. There are around 400 different types of cherry blossom tree which produce pink and white flowers. During the cherry blossom season groups of people come together to have picnics underneath the trees. This is called 'hanami', meaning 'flower viewing', and it is a custom that dates back many centuries.

YAKUTSK

Yakutsk is the coldest city in the world. January is the coldest month and the temperature doesn't reach over minus 40 degrees Celsius - that's just slightly warmer than the South Pole, where the average temperature is minus 49 degrees Celsius! A blanket of freezing cold fog covers the city most of the time, meaning that locals can only see about ten metres in front of them.

GIANT PANDA

Giant pandas are native to China and make their homes high up in the mountains. They are omnivores and have been known to eat small fish, but bamboo counts for 99% of their diet! Baby pandas are born pink and are only about the length of a pen. Sadly they are an endangered species and it's estimated that only about 1,800 of these black-and-white bears remain in the wild.

These incredible soldiers were built and buried underground over 2,000 years ago. It wasn't until 1974 that they were discovered by a group of farmers. Emperor Qin Shi Huang ordered the statues to be built so that they would protect him in his afterlife. Each warrior is made from clay and is two metres tall. None of the soldiers are the same and they are so detailed that it's possible to guess the age and rank of each one.

TERRACOTTA ARMY

BAIKAL SEALS

These seals are tiny, only growing to about 1.4 metres in length. They are native to Lake Baikal in Siberia in Russia and can dive up to 400 metres below the surface of the water. Once underwater, they use their long whiskers to find their prey and usually eat up to four kilograms of food in a single day.

FLOATING MARKETS

A floating market is a market where goods are sold from boats. They began in areas where water played a huge role in transportation. Today, most of these floating markets are tourist attractions but in the past they were hubs of community. Damnoen Saduak floating market in Thailand is the biggest market, crowded with hundreds of sellers and shoppers. Tourists come here to see the old-style and traditional way of selling and buying goods.

The Dead Sea is the lowest body of water on the surface of the Earth and sits between Israel, Jordan and Palestine. Don't let the name confuse you! This body of water is actually a lake that is almost nine times as salty as the ocean. This makes it nearly impossible for any life to survive here. Because the water is so salty, it weighs more than fresh water – this allows people to float in the Dead Sea without any effort at all!

THE DEAD SEA

SRI LANKAN ELEPHANTS

The Sri Lankan elephant is the largest of the Asian elephant family and they can grow up to roughly 3.5 metres tall and weigh up to 5,500 kilograms! They have smaller ears than African elephants which they use to keep themselves cool. They eat lots of things including roots, grass, fruit and bark, and an adult can eat up to 150 kilograms of food in just one day! Can you spot one looking for his next meal?

POHELA BOISHAKH

Pohela Boishakh is the first day of the Bengali calendar and fairs are held all over the country to celebrate. People sing and dance, puppet shows and merry-go-rounds are put on and huge colourful floats fill the streets.

The Darvaza gas crater (also called the 'Door to Hell') is a natural gas field in a collapsed underground cavern. Scientists set the gas on fire to prevent the methane gas from spreading any further and incredibly it has burnt continuously since 1971! The crater, which is 30 metres deep, is a popular tourist attraction and people have been known to go right to the edge to get a very hot look at the flames below.

ARABIAN HORSES

Arabian horses are one of the oldest breeds in the world. There are many legends and tales surrounding this breed of horse. One such story says that the prophet Muhammad picked five of his finest female horses to be the foundation of the entire Arabian breed.

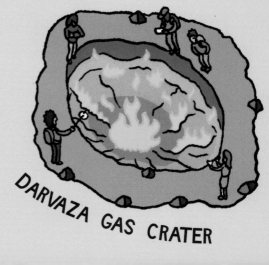

DARVAZA GAS CRATER

AUSTRALASIA

Australasia is made up of several different areas including Australia, New Zealand, Indonesia and some smaller islands. Australasia is home to a wide variety of wildlife - some, like the duck-billed platypus, can't be found anywhere else in the world! Read all about these incredible facts and then turn the page to see what you can spot.

WAVE ROCK

DUCK-BILLED PLATYPUS

This unusual-looking mammal makes its home in eastern Australia and lives near streams, rivers and lakes. With a body like an otter, a tail like a beaver and a bill and webbed feet like a duck, this creature is quite unlike anything you've seen before. It spends its time searching for food and uses its bill to scoop up worms, shrimp and insects.

The Wave Rock is exactly what it sounds like - a huge rock in the shape of a massive wave! Measuring roughly 15 metres tall and around 100 metres long the shape was formed over millions of years by weathering and water erosion.

ULURU

Located in central Australia, this enormous rock stands over 347 metres tall - almost as tall as some skyscraper buildings. Also known as Ayers Rock, it's believed to have been formed over 500 million years ago. In 1873 an explorer called William Gosse spotted the huge formation and today the rock is one of Australia's most recognisable natural landmarks.

SYDNEY OPERA HOUSE

The Sydney Opera House was designed by an architect from Denmark named Jørn Utzon. Over eight million people come to visit it every year! There are lots of different places to perform in the Opera House - the Concert Hall, the Opera Theatre, the Playhouse, the Drama Theatre, the Studio, the Forecourt and the Utzon Room. One of the world's largest organs can be found here - made up of over 10,000 pipes!

KIWIS

The kiwi is the national bird of New Zealand and this is the only place you'll find these incredible flightless birds in the wild. Their brown feathers help them blend in with the ground and keep them safe from predators, while little nostrils at the tips of their long beaks help them forage for food.

These small creatures are only found in one place in the whole world - an island called Tasmania, just off the coast of Australia. They are nocturnal creatures, which means they are active at night. Their teeth are so sharp that they can gobble up every inch of their prey... including bones! They have a funny way of telling other Tasmanian devils to back off - they sneeze! Achoo!

TASMANIAN DEVIL

MOUNT COOK

Rising over 3,700 metres up into the sky, Mount Cook is the highest mountain peak in all of New Zealand. On 3rd December in 1910, Emmeline Freda Du Faur became the first woman to climb Mount Cook.

These bizarre-looking lizards are covered head to toe in little spines and thorns which can make them look a bit menacing... but they're really very shy! These creatures live in the hot desert and, amazingly, can change colour depending on the temperature. If it's a cool day these little lizards are usually brown or grey. However, as the temperatures rise, their rough skin turns a pale orange or yellow.

THORNY DEVIL

KANGAROO ISLAND

You won't just find kangaroos on this island! Located 13 kilometres off the coast of Southern Australia, Kangaroo Island is a sanctuary for all kinds of wildlife. Barking sealions, munching koalas, clicking dolphins, buzzing bees, honking black swans and of course bouncing kangaroos can all be spotted across this incredible island.

CHRISTMAS ISLAND RED CRAB

Most of the year these red crabs lead solitary lives, busy burrowing away as they dig their way through the forest. However, come October and November, millions of these scuttling creatures migrate from the forests to the seaside to breed. During this time, Christmas island turns red as these amazing creatures cover the roads as they try to reach their destination!

Just off the coast of Queensland, Australia, lies a magical underwater world. The Great Barrier Reef is the largest coral reef system in the world - it's so big that it can even be seen from outer space. Measuring roughly 3,000 kilometres long, the Great Barrier Reef is made up of around 3,000 individual reefs and hundreds of islands. Millions of people travel from all over the world to visit this natural wonder.

THE GREAT BARRIER REEF

DINGO

Dingos are Australia's wild dogs and spend their time roaming around looking for small prey such as rabbits, birds and lizards to pounce on. They have been known to live in packs of up to ten dogs but also like to live alone. Dingos don't bark like other dogs do. Instead, they communicate with each other using wolf-like howls.

ANTARCTICA

Antarctica is a freezing cold, windswept desert, surrounded by the icy Southern Ocean. Most of the continent is covered in ice over one kilometre thick and conditions are so harsh that there are no permanent residents on the island. However, a number of plants and animals don't seem to mind these extreme conditions and have made this icy place their home. Read all about this freezing continent and then turn the page and see what you can find.

EMPEROR PENGUINS

Emperor penguins are the biggest of all the different kinds of penguins and can grow to about 115 centimetres tall (about the same size as a six-year-old). These black, white and yellow penguins spend their entire life in the freezing Antarctica where temperatures can drop as low as minus 50 degrees Celsius! They have large stores of body fat and several layers of little feathers that protect them against the icy Antarctic winds.

BLUE WHALES

Everything about these creatures is huge. They can grow up to 30 metres long, weigh more than 200 tonnes and can live up to 90 years. They are the largest animals ever known to have lived on Earth and their tongues alone can weigh as much as an elephant. They spend their time feasting on the Antarctic krill in the icy waters before migrating to warmer waters to breed.

THE HALLEY VI RESEARCH STATION

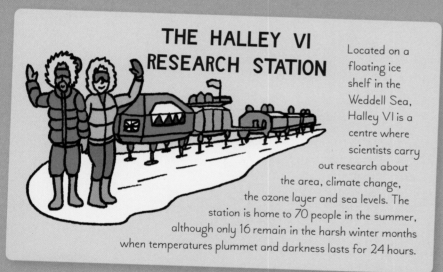

Located on a floating ice shelf in the Weddell Sea, Halley VI is a centre where scientists carry out research about the area, climate change, the ozone layer and sea levels. The station is home to 70 people in the summer, although only 16 remain in the harsh winter months when temperatures plummet and darkness lasts for 24 hours.

HOLY TRINITY CHURCH

When you think of Antarctica you might think of snow, penguins, seals and freezing cold winds. You might not think of churches... but believe it or not, there are *eight* churches in Antarctica! Holy Trinity Church, finished in 2004, is one of these. It is made out of wood, can fit 30 people inside and is just 15 metres tall. The tiny church has even played host to a wedding – in 2007 Chilean and Russian researchers tied the knot, making for a very frosty wedding!

LEOPARD SEAL

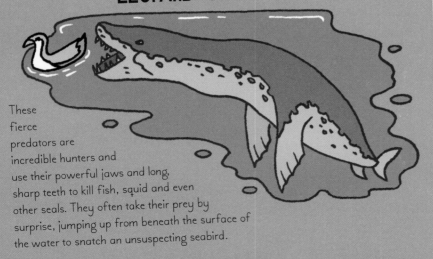

These fierce predators are incredible hunters and use their powerful jaws and long, sharp teeth to kill fish, squid and even other seals. They often take their prey by surprise, jumping up from beneath the surface of the water to snatch an unsuspecting seabird.

ORCA WHALES

These marine beasts, also called killer whales, hunt almost everything – fish, seals, penguins, turtles, squid and even sharks – and can consume over 200 kilograms of food a day. They have around 45 teeth, which they use to capture their prey.

ROSS ICE SHELF

Discovered by Captain James Clark Ross, the Ross Ice Shelf is the world's largest body of floating ice and is roughly the same size as France. It is hundreds of metres thick and is fed by a constant supply of ice from glaciers draining onto it. The area is quite flat and because of this, many Antarctica expeditions have used the Ross Ice Shelf as a base camp.

COLOSSAL SQUID

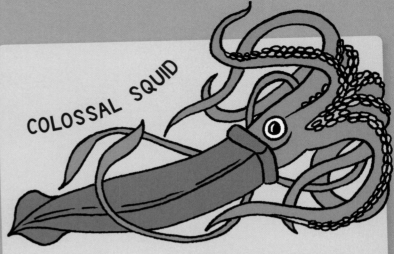

Unlike the giant squid who only has suckers and small teeth along its tentacles, the colossal squid's limbs also have razor sharp hooks. It is the biggest squid in the word and can grow to around 14 metres tall. Its eyes are equally enormous, measuring 40 centimetres in diameter - about the same size as a beach ball! Not very much is known about this eight-armed beast but it's believed to hunt using bioluminescence (the production of light to attract prey).

KRILL

Antarctic krill are tiny little creatures, about the size of a paperclip. They live in huge groups of up to 10,000 krill per cubic metre. There are over *500 million tonnes* of krill in the Southern Ocean and they can live up to ten years - although living that long can be difficult when you're a giant blue whale's favourite meal. The giant creatures can consume up to 40 million krill in just one day!

Found on Ross Island, this active volcano is just under 4,000 metres tall, and at the top a swirling pool of lava rumbles and bubbles. It's hard to imagine something being so hot in the freezing cold Antarctica, but the lava lake is over 900 degrees Celsius and the volcano produces a few mini eruptions every day! It is the most southern active volcano in the world and in the right conditions it's possible to see the glow from the lava lake against the sky.

MOUNT EREBUS

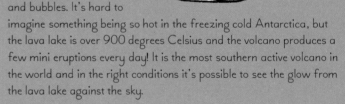

Deception Island, situated off the coast of Antarctica, is home to several research stations but is also a major tourist attraction. It was formed about 10,000 years ago when a huge volcano erupted and then collapsed in on itself, forming the horseshoe-shaped island. The area contains a number of geothermally heated pools which tourists have been known to take a dip in!

DECEPTION ISLAND

Not all penguins waddle - rockhopper penguins hop from place to place! But it isn't just their hopping that sets them apart from other penguins - they also have rock-star cool hair. Their distinct little tufts of yellow feathers, bright orange beaks and wonderfully pink feet set them apart from the rest of the crowd.

ROCKHOPPER PENGUINS

ANSWERS

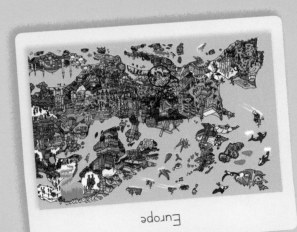

Europe

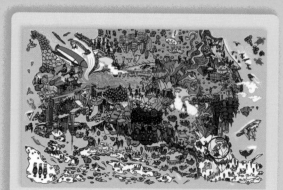

North America

Asia

Australasia

Africa

South America

Antarctica

Catch Cat © 2019 Quarto Publishing plc.
Text © 2019 Quarto Publishing plc. Illustrations © 2019 Andy Council.
Words by Claire Grace

First Published in 2019 by Wide Eyed Editions, an imprint of The Quarto Group.
The Old Brewery, 6 Blundell Street, London N7 9BH, United Kingdom.
T (0)20 7700 6700 F (0)20 7700 8066 **www.QuartoKnows.com**

The right of Andy Council to be identified as the illustrator has been asserted by him in accordance with the Copyright, Designs and Patents Act, 1988 (UK).

All rights reserved.

A catalogue record for this book is available from the British Library.

ISBN 978-1-78603-765-7

The illustrations were created using pen and ink, and were coloured digitally.
Set in Boring Boron, Mrs Lollipop and Pistacho

Published by Rachel Williams and Jenny Broom
Designed by Nicola Price • Edited by Claire Grace • Production by Nicolas Zeifman

Manufactured in Printplus PP, China PP0519

9 8 7 6 5 4 3 2 1

Brimming with creative inspiration, how-to projects, and useful information to enrich your everyday life, Quarto Knows is a favourite destination for those pursuing their interests and passions. Visit our site and dig deeper with our books into your area of interest: Quarto Creates, Quarto Cooks, Quarto Homes, Quarto Lives, Quarto Drives, Quarto Explores, Quarto Gifts, or Quarto Kids.

Quarto
Knows

MIX
Paper from
responsible sources
FSC
www.fsc.org
FSC® C001701